HEINEMANN GUIDED READERS

STARTER LEVEL

JOHN MILNE

Lucky Number

HEINEMANN

Café Colombo is always busy. There are
always people sitting at the tables in
Café Colombo. The men and women
are all well-dressed. They drink coffee.
They eat ice-cream. They read
newspapers.

Charlie does not sit in Café Colombo.
Charlie is not well-dressed. He sits on
the pavement outside Café Colombo.
He sits on a small box.

Charlie is a shoeshine boy. Charlie
shines shoes. He does not go to school.
He works all day.

3

Charlie shines men's shoes. He shines
ladies' shoes. He shines black shoes. He
shines brown shoes. He shines blue
shoes.

Shoeshine! Shoeshine!
Ten cents! Ten cents!
Ten cents a shine!

A man in Café Colombo shouts,
'Charlie!'

Charlie runs into Café Colombo. He
puts his box at the man's feet. The man
puts one foot on the box.

The man's shoes are black. The man's
shoes are dirty. Charlie cleans the man's
shoes.

The man gives Charlie ten cents.
Charlie takes the ten cent coin. He
picks up his box. He goes back to the
pavement.

An old man walks slowly along the
pavement. The old man is carrying a
large board. There is a notice on the
board. The old man is selling lottery
tickets.

A well-dressed man in Café Colombo is shouting.

The ticket-seller gives the man a ticket. The man gives the ticket-seller a dollar.

9

The well-dressed man is in a hurry. A taxi is waiting. The man puts the ticket in his pocket quickly.

The man gets into the taxi. The ticket falls out of his pocket. The wind blows the ticket into the air.

Charlie catches the ticket. He has the ticket in his hand.

Charlie waves his arms. He shouts out loudly.

The man does not hear Charlie. The taxi moves away. Charlie stands on the pavement. The ticket is in his hand.

Café Colombo closes at midnight.
Charlie's home is far away. Every night,
Charlie has a long walk home.

Charlie's mother is waiting for him. He
gives her all the money.

Charlie has no father. Charlie has
younger brothers and younger sisters.
Charlie's mother needs the money. She
buys food with the money.

Charlie shows his mother the lottery ticket. His mother looks at the ticket.

She reads the number – SEVEN – FIVE – THREE – EIGHT – ONE – TWO – NINE – FOUR – SIX.

Is this the winning number? Perhaps it is. Saturday 21st is tomorrow. Perhaps tomorrow will be their lucky day!

LUCKY NUMBERS

SERIE 041 753 812 946

FIND OUT THE WINNER ON SATURDAY 21st

Charlie is tired. He puts the ticket on his box. He falls asleep.

Charlie has a dream.

A goat comes into the house. The goat finds the ticket. The goat is eating the ticket.

The goat eats the number six.
The goat eats the number four.
The goat eats the number nine.

Charlie wakes up. It is morning. The ticket is not on the box! Where is the ticket?

Charlie runs to the lottery office. Charlie sees his mother. She has the ticket!

A man is shouting out the winning number.

Seven – five – three – eight – one – two – nine – four —

Will the next number be six? Will it be their lucky number? Will it be their lucky day?